ROCKY AND SANDY

ROCKY AND SANDY

THE STORY OF TWO TORTOISES
ON THE CALIFORNIA DESERT

THE WARD RITCHIE PRESS

PHOTOGRAPHY BY BERNIE AND CYNTHIA CRAMPTON
STORY BY MARJORIE RANKIN STEURT

DEDICATED

TO ALL TORTOISES
ON THE CALIFORNIA & ARIZONA DESERTS;
AND TO ALL OF US
WHO THRILL TO THE WONDER AND DELIGHT
THESE DESERT ANIMALS GIVE US.

Rocky pecked at his shell.

Ah, it cracked.

Then a piece fell out. And another piece.

Now his head and one leg felt the warm desert sunshine.

He worked hard.

Soon he was free of the round, white shell.

Rocky, the desert tortoise, was born.

He looked around his desert home.

There was no mother to take care of him. She had laid
the eggs in the warm sand and then crawled away.

Rocky never saw her.

Reptiles do not care for their babies.

Rocky and his brothers and sisters had to take care
of themselves.

As soon as he pecked his way out of his
    shell, he could crawl.
He didn't have to learn.
Something clear down in his tiny body told him how.
We call this instinct.

Instinct also taught him what to eat.
There was no mother to feed him milk. In fact
    tortoise babies don't drink milk.
As soon as he was born he started to nibble on
    grass and leaves and cactus.

The shell that covered his body, top and bottom, was
    like rubber.
If he heard a man coming he had to crawl under a
    rock or bush.
Instinct told him those big feet could crush him.
But month by month his shell hardened.
By the time he was two years old it was like a rock.
That is why we named him Rocky.

Tortoises live to be over a hundred years old.

So Rocky had plenty of time to grow up. In fact, it
took him nine whole years.

He crawled around in the desert, ate grass and leaves
and cactus, and grew.

But he didn't have to go to school as you and I do.

Instinct taught him what he had to know.

When he was grown and his shell had hardened, he
knew nothing could crush it.
So when he heard an enemy coming, he no longer had
to hide. He simply pulled his head and feet
into his shell.

Now that he was grown, Rocky was lonely. Instinct
    told him he wanted a mate.
Finally he saw Sandy crawling across the desert
    ahead of him.
Maybe this was the mate he was looking for.
He followed her hoping
She would like him.

At last she turned and faced him.

She didn't crawl away.

It was her way of saying, "Yes, I like you."

Rocky led Sandy into the section of the desert
    he called home.
Here they lay on the warm sand near each other.
Now neither was lonely.
They were both very happy.

From then on they went everywhere together.

Rocky showed Sandy where the juiciest grass was.

He took her to the tastiest cactus.

He showed her where to crawl under shelter when
the blazing desert sun was too hot.
This is something else instinct had taught Rocky.
He couldn't sweat as you and I do when we're hot.
Even if he pulled his head and feet into his shell,
it was still hot.
So he and Sandy found shade to lie in during the
middle of the day.

Or, on still hotter days, he dug a hole in the shade
    for them to snuggle into.
Here it was quite cool.

In the late afternoon, when the sun was low, they
crawled out and lay side by side.
All of this was the happy way they passed their
days in the piece of desert they called home.

And then suddenly one day Rocky saw another male
tortoise coming into his home ground.
This meant trouble.

The stranger went right up to Sandy.

He was trying to take her away from Rocky.

Rocky knew he couldn't meet this danger by crawling
into his shell.
He'd have to fight to keep the stranger from
walking off with Sandy.

But the stranger wanted Sandy and he was
    willing to fight for her.
Crash, the two shells met with an awful clash.
Bang, bang, bang.
Rocky pulled in his head, but the crashing of the
    shells shook his whole body.

Sandy stood in the tall grass watching anxiously.

She would have to go with the winner.

But she wanted to stay with Rocky.

If she could have spoken she would have yelled,

"Rocky, get him, Rocky."

Rocky knew she was watching.

He fought harder and harder.

His front feet tangled with the stranger's feet.

Bang, bang, bang, their shells crashed together.

Finally Rocky dug his hind feet into the sand.
He shoved his shell under the stranger's shell
    and gave a mighty heave.
The stranger flipped over on his back.
His legs waved in the air.
But he was helpless.

Rocky had won, but the stranger was still here
    on Rocky's home ground.
Rocky was angry. Would he have to fight again?
The stranger struggled, his feet waving in the air.
Rocky watched him carefully.

The stranger kicked his feet and rocked his body
   back and forth.
Finally he managed to turn over.
He was on his feet now, but he looked terribly
   tired.
Rocky stood right beside him ready to fight
   again if necessary.

But there was no more fight left in the stranger.

He knew he was beaten.

Slowly he crawled away.

Rocky followed close behind him.

He wanted to make sure the stranger left this part
of the desert he and Sandy called home.

When the stranger had gone Rocky returned to Sandy.

He lay down beside her to rest.

Safe once more, they were both happy.

Then the time came for Sandy to lay her eggs.

She chose a level spot in the hot sun and dug a
hole in the warm sand.

Here she laid her eggs and covered them carefully,
using her feet to scoop the sand back over them.

Then she smoothed the spot so no enemy could find it.

Rocky stayed at a distance.

The egg-laying was entirely Sandy's affair.

But when she had finished he led her tenderly
to the tall green grass. Here she ate and ate.

She never returned to her eggs.

She knew the warm sun would hatch them and the
babies could take care of themselves.

Finally, in the fall, the nights grew cold.

Our warm blood keeps us warm. But tortoises are
cold-blooded animals like snakes and lizards.

Instinct again told them what to do.

Rocky chose a spot well hidden by bushes.

Here he dug a slanting burrow deep into the
ground.

When finished he and Sandy crawled in and went
to sleep.

Here, safe from all enemies, they slept through
the cold winter months.

Here it was snug and warm.

This is called hibernation.

All through the winter their piece of desert lay
    empty and still.
Their neighbors the snakes and lizards hibernated too.

But when spring came the sun once again warmed
    the desert sand.
Rocky and Sandy woke up, crawled out of their hole,
    and started looking for juicy grasses.
They were very hungry after their long winter fast.
And oh, it was wonderful to be out in the sunny
    world again.